THROUGH THE EYES OF A CHILD

OF A CHILD

A Story Of Domestic Violence

LATOYA ROBINSON

LaToya Robinson

THROUGH THE EYES OF
A CHILD

CONTENTS

This book is dedicated to my beautiful
mother may you rest in peace in heaven
with no more heartache, pain or worries
we will forever cherish, honor, and
remember you, your spirit, and your
memories Love you always.

CHAPTER 1

"The Beginning"

I love her, she so pretty and smart, she would never let anything happen to me. She would never let anyone hurt me in any kind of way, so why does she let him hurt her? I hate when he hurts her, I wish I could do something- protect her, just make him stop. I wish we could run away so we can be happy all the time. I don't sleep when this happens. I stay up I listen I watch, I wait for the sound that lets me know I should run in there or maybe call the police (I'm going to do it one day). When it is too quiet I worry! I put my ear to the wall, I walk the hall, put my ear to the door listening for signs of movement, breathing, talking, LIFE. The next day I pretend I don't feel well and couldn't sleep so that I don't have to go to school. Of course they know I'm lying but because they know what happen last night no one questions it. Hell I always felt my mother found comfort in me staying home and he's not going to say anything because no sooner than the rage comes it leaves and now he is in apology, feeling sorry, let me fix it mode. That's when the gifts and the I'm sorry I will never do it again comes and she accepts. Things are back to normal for a while until it happens again, and the cycle just repeats itself.

Why don't she just leave, does she really believe he will never do it again?

She took the physical hits but I was hit emotionally every time I heard her yell or cry out "please stop no you're hurting me" As soon as I hear the first loud noise, something that breaks or hit's the floor hard, my heart is pounding, the tears automatically start to flow. I run to where they are I scream stop don't do it you said you weren't going to do it anymore, as my mom tries to calmly say it's ok baby go back to your room. Every once in a while if I get there in time I can stop it, I would grab on to my mom and hold on tight. I would tell her I'm not letting go I'm not leaving out this room, and it would work but sometimes I'm too late.

I have always had a fear of losing my mother even as a young child. My mother was a victim of domestic violence in just about every relationship she was in and my brother and I were along for the ride. I believe it affected us both in very different ways. For me I seem to always replay situations over in my mind like flash backs. I am a child under the age of 10 and I am thinking of ways I can protect my mother. By the time I was a teenager I am thinking straight up murder because I am tired of seeing her hit. So let me just tell you some what about the beginning of my mothers journey with domestic violence through my eyes. I can remember being so little thinking run mommy and never come back. I would sleep light just in case the night would come that she would want to leave, like a thief in the night I would be ready. She finally got the courage to leave my father and risk not having his support financially but it was time to take that risk, because being hit is no comfort either. She had left my father a few times before and always went back but this time she left for good.

Then she meets Carl and he seems ok, but it's just something about him that I can't put my finger on. I was a very suspicious child by nature and paid attention to everything, so you see I had a funny kind of eerie feeling about him. We lived down the street from his Uncle Mr. Johnny and he was very nice. He always gave us sweets and he and my mother would talk about everything as she helped him with his garden. Mr. Johnny had a very nice back yard with a big garden and flowers, and he loved to have company because he had loss his wife and didn't have many friends.

One night my mother and Carl was arguing and it sent chills up my spine. The next thing I hear is my mother scream as she fell down the stairs and hit her face on the wall. I know he pushed her but I didn't see him do it- I just knew he did it, he was standing right there with this creepy smile on his face. When he seen me looking he said look at you girl you den fell down the stairs, he looked at me and said your mama ok she just clumsy and went in his room. I ran to her, she was holding her hand up against her face and she said I'm ok baby I just fell. The next morning my mother eye looked horrible with a gash under it. After that other than saying good morning or hi, I never really talked to him again. My feelings was right he is a bad man that's why he always gave me the creeps. I didn't tell my mother how I felt but she knew something because she would always say you know you can talk to me about anything

, I don't care what it's about. I knew she was saying that because she noticed I didn't talk to Carl anymore and I said I'm fine, I just don't like to talk to people who hurt my mama.

When Carl left for his normal weekend getaway we walked down the street to visit Mr. Johnny like we usually do except this time mama had her sunglasses on. Mr. Johnny was happy for the visit as always and couldn't wait to start gossiping and pulling out the snacks he had bought for us. He noticed mama didn't take her sunglasses off and he joked those must be some nice glasses you don't even want to take them off. I guess he couldn't take it anymore (you know how old people are set in their ways) He said girl take them glasses off in the house. Mama slowly took the glasses off and he said "oh no girl Carl did this didn't he" and she replied I fell down the stairs. He looked at her in anguish and finally said did you happen to fall after you and Carl had been arguing, honey you don't deserve that. You need to get away from him Carl destroys everything he comes in contact with, he is crazy. Mr. Johnny said y'all kids go play now, he wanted to have what he called grown people talk. I guess he let my mother in on a little secret about Carl's weekend getaways. I heard her telling my grandmother about it and it didn't surprise me at all, Carl was crazy as hell. He had a lot of issues and was going to Northville every weekend and everybody knows Northville is where crazy people go. Whatever he was doing there was enough to scare her and shortly after that she left Carl. She never told us kids why she left and we never asked either, at least I didn't.

CHAPTER 2

"Here We go Again"

The summer goes by and its almost time for school to start, so my mother picks my brother and I up from our fathers house and she has a surprise. She introduces us to her new boyfriend Ron who is driving this big pretty Cadillac. My brother is amazed with it, because he likes cars so Ron is using that to get my brother to open up. Ron buys us McDonalds and anything we want out the store before we get home. He is going on and on about how he likes kids and we gone have so much fun. I'm thinking ok this sounds good he may be cool. Then mama hits us with the surprise, she said we got a new house and ya'll going to a new school and things are going to be good I promise.

Once we got to the house it took a minute but I figured out oh, Ron stay here too, so I wonder how this gone be. A couple of weeks later mama and Ron set us down and told us they are planning on getting married. Ron wanted to know if it was ok with us first. We kids what do we know, all we knew was so far this guy was ok. I mean it wasn't like we knew him

7

a long time or something we just basically met him. So like most little kids do they follow their parents lead and we said yea that's ok. Plus my mother seemed like she was very happy, the happiest I had seen her in a while. I didn't get a creepy feeling from him like I did Carl so that was a good thing. Ron was like a big kid and so far what he said was true he really did like kids plus him and mama got along good.

Eventually they got married and we moved into Ron's mother house after she passed away. Things were really seeming good, he had some rules but they weren't crazy or anything like that. We had sit downs and family discussions when we went over rules or what was to be expected of us kids. I really liked that because it wasn't like he was just telling us what to do. Anyway, mama made most of the rules up and it was like he kind of followed her lead on that kind of stuff. He did have one request though he wasn't a fan of the word stepfather or stepdad and did not want to be called that. He asked if we would call him Ron or dad, which ever one we were comfortable with was ok with him just not stepfather. We have settled into the house and neighborhood and everything seems great.

Just as I am about to go to sleep one night I hear yelling. I lay there very still just listening thinking what's about to happen. I'm getting scared I knew it was too good to be true. It wasn't the first time they argued it just was the first time at night and it seemed different this time. Eventually they stopped arguing and the daylight finally came. They started to have more and more of those arguments and of course it eventually turned physical. When things would happen in the daytime it was more embarrassing then scary but when its nighttime it was scary to me. It's like everybody is supposed to be asleep, no one else knows this is happening. I'm thinking if I have to call the police how fast will they come. Please just let the sun come up and they will quiet down cause more people are listening and I know my grandma is woke.

The men in my mothers life always had good jobs and took care of her financially. In the old days that is what mattered and you would hear women say "as long as a man is taking care of home and you don't want for nothing, then a man gone be a man", and there is certain thing you just have to deal with. Which meant if they cheat or hit you, you just shut your mouth and take it because he is providing. That old saying right there has made a lot of women stay in situations that have been very unhealthy. I would hear people talking about the material things my mother had and saying "you lucky you got a good man". In some cases he was a good man, he paid the bills, she didn't have to work, he kept money in her pocket, he took care of her kids. On payday she would go to his job and he would give her his whole paycheck and she would give him an allowance. He always bought her nice gifts, jewelry, and cars. After he would jump on her he would buy her an expensive piece of jewelry or upgrade her car. So that's a good man I thought umm, I don't know but this just seems twisted some how. Why don't adults see it or is this really how relationships are supposed to be?

I was awaken in the middle of the night and told to get

dress my brother and I are going to my dad's (stepfather) brother house until the morning. My mother wasn't feeling good and needed to go to the hospital. I immediately was scared something didn't feel right and I knew they weren't telling us everything. I didn't think I was going to see my mother again. The morning came and my dad picked us up and my mother was in the car. I was so happy I just started crying and she said what's wrong baby. We ran to the car ready to hug her trying to grab her through the window but she put her hand out to stop us. At the same time looking as if she was bracing herself for the impact in case we didn't stop in time. She was moving like she was very stiff like she was not trying to turn all the way around to look at us in the back seat. She said I'm ok guys I love you but you have to be real careful around me for the next couple of days. What's wrong we asked and she said I just had an accident and I'm a little sore.

I knew something wasn't right because my dad wasn't really talking and he had that look on his face he always had when he did something wrong. When he did talk to her it was real gentle like you would talk to a baby or like in a tone that's very sympathetic as if he was saying sorry every time he spoke. I finally figured out what happened when I heard my mother talking to my grandmother. He shot her in the back and she was trying to tell my grandmother it was an accident. She said it was a bullet that ricochet from outside. It was very hard for me to sleep after I heard that, and when I did I would sleep walk ending up next to my mothers bed. Things were very quiet for a while and we had a lot of good times after that. We just act like it never happened, they never even talked to us about it. The only time we would hear about it, is when they are arguing and my mother yells it out "you shot me in my back you dirty muthafucka".

Knowing that he shot her changed me, I became more alert more defensive. I never had to call the police yet, but I always knew if I had too I would. I also felt like it was my job to know when to call the police. Most of the time it would be an argument, you might hear a crash like furniture moving or her crying and I pretty much knew what was happening. In the morning I would see her and she would have a puffy eye or cut lip. She would say I'm ok and I would look with tears and concern in my eyes and say ok I love you ma. My mind would be racing I don't know what to do, I want to hurt him that's my mother but I do nothing. I feel like a punk like I failed her.

A child growing up in a domestic violence situation learns early that the rules are a little bit different at home. Children are taught at a young age about 911, and to call when there is a fire or someone is hurt, or just when you need help. But see this where it gets tricky because what about when daddy is hurting mommy! You learn in those situations you don't call the police because then he will get in trouble and "we don't want him to get in trouble", besides everything is o.k. The few times you do call the police you almost feel bad in a way. You see the shame on your mothers face as the police talk to her and shine the flashlight in her face to see if there are bruises. Your father is saying he didn't do anything and it must be a misunderstanding that the police are even here. I was just talking to my wife, we may have yelled a little but that's all, right baby as he looks at your mother and she says yes. Then the officer looks at you and say is that right, are you o.k.?

Silence comes over the room as it feels like everyone is staring at you. You are froze with nerves and your mind is racing. What do I say, do I tell the truth or do I lie as you scan the room looking at everybody face. It seems like you have been standing there for hours and it's been seconds maybe a minute or two then you blurt out I don't know and bury your face in your mothers lap. It feels like a weight is lifted off you when one of the police officers say "this is what we are going to do, someone has to leave for the night ". If we come back out here tonight somebody is going to jail. If there is no noticeable bruising or marks or she is not really saying too much as if she may be scared but is still insisting she is not pressing charges, they will strongly suggest her and the kids leave for the night. They offer rides to family member homes or hotels or they stay until you grab a change of clothes for you and the kids and they watch you and the kids get in your car and pull off. Even though you know you did the right thing by calling the police you feel like maybe you shouldn't have because your mother is still sad. You start to think to yourself dang did I just make her feel worse.

There were a few times when things got bad we left and went to my grandmother house or even a shelter but we never stayed long we always went back. When we did go to a shelter, those were times that she was tired, didn't want my grandma to know, and or fed up, nobody wants to be a punching bag. Those were scary times because everything is so hush hush, the places are very secretive and they don't want you telling anyone where you are. The locations are kept private for your safety as well as the safety of the other women and children that are there. Sometimes you do hear very bad stories of what women have experienced from the men that say they love them. Sometimes the fear from the other women of if their spouse were to find them and what they would do would be enough for my mom to say we just gone leave because my situation is not that bad. My mother would say "these women really need help, they are really scared". Denial is a big part of Domestic Violence, the victim does not see their situation as that bad, so going back seems like the right thing to do. If she stayed that would be admitting that her situation is pretty bad too.

Sometimes the reason we would go back would be as simple as, they made contact with each other and that's all it would take. He would apologize sometimes even cry, I guess he just knew what to say or do to get her back. After the shooting incident my grandma would tell my mother not to go back when she would leave. She would say to her he gone kill you one day. Then my mother would stand firm on going back, telling my grandma she just didn't understand. My grandma would become so angry with her, but she was always there for her the next time and the next time after that too.

CHAPTER 3

"Confused"

When it was time for me to graduate from elementary school (6th grade) I never made it to the ceremony. It was one of those times when they were broken up and we were staying at my grandmothers house. See the problem was the school is right around the corner from our house. You had to pass the house to get to the school if you walked down the street we lived on. I told my mother that I didn't care if I went to graduation or not, I only said that because I knew something was going to happen, everything was too quiet. He had stopped calling her back to back and telling her to come home so they can talk, it just seemed strange to me. Deep down in my gut I just felt something wasn't right, that's not normal for him to do when she leaves. Either he hurt, in jail, or he planning something. So I thought if I said I didn't want to go she would say ok and that she didn't have to try and be brave for me. My mother looked at me and said you are going to your graduation, you are not going to let this grown up mess ruin your day. My grandmother had got me this pretty white dress, it was covered with this lace pattern and it was just beautiful. I didn't even like dresses but I wanted to wear this one, so this was a special moment.

The day of my graduation is here and we are walking down the street, as we get close to the house my heart starts to race and I'm thinking just let everything be ok. Just like I thought he pops out the house saying let me talk to you. She is saying hell no you can't talk to me along with some other choice words and he is doing the usual pleading for her to talk to him. I'm standing there thinking we should have kept walking, why did we stop, this is not going to be good. In the midst of them arguing back and fourth he manages to tell me you look pretty baby girl and acknowledges that it's my graduation day. You would think at that moment they both would have stopped and said lets let this girl go to her graduation but nope they continued. This is one of the confusing parts about Domestic Violence, the women go back sometimes or the men say they should come back because it's better for the kids to be at home but who is thinking about the kids when the Violence is happening!!!

People are walking pass on their way to the graduation asking is everything ok, I was embarrassed because I knew some of the kids. Some of the adults walking pass new my parents and grew up with my stepfather, so needless to say everybody is going to know. I don't know what I missed but all of a sudden he started to walk like he was about to come out the gate and my mother just grabbed my hand and took off running. He started running behind us and he must have not closed the gate because our dogs were running behind him. When we got to the major street we had to cross I let her hand go as we were running across the street. I slipped and fell in the middle lane because I had those slippery dress shoes on. She was running fast so she didn't realize I had fell, I guess she kept running because she knew he wouldn't do anything to me.

Across the street was a little restaurant that had a little brick wall along the front of the parking lot and it looked like she was going to try and climb over it. I was stuck in the yellow lane by the traffic and I lost sight of her when I looked back to my dad(stepfather) calling my name while he was crossing the street. He stopped to ask me if I was ok and why was I running. As we made it to the other side of the street I simply replied I don't know I was trying to keep up with mama. He said did you see which way she went I said no. The dogs were running wild as if we were playing a game. He said I have to go get the dogs and see which way your mama went, go back to the house and wait everything will be ok. I said ok and stood there like I was waiting for traffic to clear so I could cross the street. When he got further down the side street where the restaurant sat and he was out of sight I walked inside the restaurant. I must have been looking confused because just as I was about to ask the lady at the window if I could use the phone, she said "are you looking for your mama", I said yes. My mother peeked around and said that's my daughter, the lady quickly said come back here and opened the door to the back. My mother was crying and upset, she asked me why did I stop running, I said I fell and she said I'm sorry baby.

One of the ladies that worked there said I saw you talking

to a man was that him, I said yes. My mother asked did he see you come in here and what did he say to you? I said no, he just told me to go home and wait he was going to look for you and get the dogs because they were running all around. Then one of the ladies asked my mother did she have someone to call or did she want to call the police, and the other lady yelled out I'm calling the police. My mother still had tears in her eyes as she looked at the lady and said ok to her calling the police. The police came and took us down to the station and they began to ask my mother a bunch of questions. Because he didn't hit her or do anything they said it was really nothing they could do. They did say she could file for a restraining order if he is harassing her. My mother just sat there for a minute and then asked if she could use the phone to call someone to pick us up. The officer said yes and he also asked her if she knew what she going to do as far as the restraining order and she said she will think about it.

My uncle came to pick us up and take us back to my grandma's house and my mother is telling him the story on the way there. As my mother was telling him what happened he looked back at me and said "niece you alright". I said yea but what I really wanted to say was no and bust out crying but I felt it would only make the situation seem worse and make my mother feel sadder than she already does. When we got to my grandma house everybody was sitting on the porch. I felt embarrassed to get out the car because I had fell and my stockings were kind of ripped and my dress was dirty. My grandmother looked at me and said to my mother "did y'all make it to the graduation". Before my mother could say anything I walked pass my grandmother and said I didn't want to wear this stupid dress anyway. I heard my mother say no we never made it, he started his bull shit when we walked pass the house. My grandmother yelled out my mothers name in despair and said what happened. When they came in the house to hear what happened, I thought wow now she has to tell the story all over again and everybody is going to be asking me questions. After she finished telling what happened my grandmother asked her what was she going to do, and my mother said she didn't know she just wished everyone would stop asking her that.

The summer goes by and it was ok I guess, I still got to see my best friend so that was cool. She was like another granddaughter to my grandma so she would come over there and visit me. I guess I'm going to school from my grandma house because my mother hasn't said anything about us going home. So I'm starting to get nervous because I have to start a new school and I'm already not quick to make friends so this should be fun. Although I think maybe it could be ok because no one knows about what happened at graduation and nobody will be fighting over here, at least not my parents. So when my mother comes to talk to me about starting a new school and ask me my feelings on it, I just say I don't really have any feelings on it. I said of course I don't want to have to meet new people and she said you will be ok, it's good to meet new people. She just didn't understand, me and the few people I had grown to know from elementary were all going to the same middle school so that transition from elementary to middle school would be easy. At the end of day I felt like my feelings didn't matter anyway, so I just kept it short. Maybe starting this new school won't be all that bad I know a few people from my grandma's neighborhood, plus I don't want to give my mother any excuse to feel like she needs to go back to him.

As soon as I start to settle in and get into the routine of things around my grandma house and at school, guess what we are going back. That's why I stay to myself because it's too much back and fourth. I wonder does my mother even notice I am becoming an awkward child. Now we are back and acting like everything is back to normal. Now I have that anxiety back about what if someone ask where I been at or why didn't I start school with everybody else. On top of that what's messed up is I didn't get a chance to learn the school with everybody else, so now I'm going to look like a newbie when I was supposed to be there in the first place. I'm also feeling awkward in my own home because I don't know how I should act around Ron. I'm thinking should I forget about it, I do miss being at home and mama seems like she is happy. When kids do something wrong parents are suppose to let them know they did wrong and they are upset with them, so should kids do the same with parents. I don't want to be disrespectful and get in trouble but I do want to let him know how I feel, but if I do, that will just start everything back up. Everyone seems happy and settled back in just like nothing ever happened. Finally a few days later he comes in the living room and say I just want y'all to know I'm glad you back home, me and your mama gone be ok. We just say ok we glad we home too and keep watching tv, I mean what else we supposed to say. I had so much to say but I'm just a kid and I don't want to start trouble when we doing good. My parents just tried to act like we were over my grandma house for summer vacation or something.

CHAPTER 4

"A Frustrated Mind"

There were a few arguments here and there over the next couple of months but nothing real serious. When voices were raised I would get up and go in their room half asleep ad say "I heard something". My mother would always say its ok, and my stepfather would say baby girl I'm sorry are we too loud. I would say don't fight please and it would work sometimes, they would stop arguing. I would get up the next morning and act like I didn't remember, thinking that would help make things better. I would think to myself they did stop arguing so whatever the problem was I don't want to bring it back up.

Outside of my best friend that lived down the street from me I really was kind of nervous about anyone coming over to my house. Even when things were good in the back of my mind I didn't want anyone to figure out what was going on behind close doors. Which I didn't know why I felt that way, because 99% of the time everything bad happened at night, so it probably would have been ok. I guess I figured if I let them come over during the day, eventually they would probably say we should have a sleep over at my house because during the day my house did seem fun. My parents were kind of cool and everyone loved my mom, my stepfather was a big kid at heart. When its kids around he is going to go get us fast food, candy, play games or give us money to do stuff. To me it was just kind of confusing, if he could pretend when people are around why couldn't he figure out a way to stop acting like that at night. For some reason they really did feel like it didn't affect me, probably because I never got hit or abused. To me it was like me getting hit because it was my mother and when she hurt I hurt. I also played it off a lot, like it didn't bother me because I guess I just cared more about their feelings than mine. Plus who wants to be the kid that ruined the family.

When I would see her black eye, bruised body and or just emotionally beat down and drained the next morning my fear turns to anger. How can he do this to a person he said he loves and he is supposed to protect her not hurt her. Is he really about to say good morning to me like nothing happened, how rude that's my mother you just put your hands on. I do as a child is supposed to do and I say good morning. You want me to take to you to school today he would ask, nope I replied I'm not going I couldn't sleep. He apologizes to me for me not being able to sleep but not for what he did to my mother. Mom would get a new car or piece of jewelry within a couple of days, my brother and I would get new stuff and things would settle down. I would want things to be back to normal so, I act like everything is ok but really it's not. I would take the things he would buy but, I would feel as if I'm saying its ok to hit my mother.

I just want her to leave sometimes but, I don't know how to say it because, I'm young and I don't want to embarrass my mother she has been through enough. Then sometimes I think what if she leaves him and gets with someone worse. He's not all that bad if he would just stop hitting her everything would be fine. We have so much fun and it's so nice on the good days almost like the Huxtables, if only it could be like this all the time. The crazy thing is I had a good childhood. I know there is probably many kids that would have loved to grow up in my household. That's the crazy thing about Domestic Violence the person doing the hurting is usually someone everyone in the house loves but eventually will hate. I think parents sometimes forget that from the day a child is born they love their mothers. If my mother was happy and in a good place no matter what was going on I knew it would be ok, but if she was sad I was sad.

One time we were in a shelter for battered women that was right by the house and I just knew someone was going to see us, but if they did nobody mentioned it. My best friend always told me I worried too much, and that nobody knows and kids don't care about stuff like that anyway, they will still be your friend. It was nice having her to talk to, she always knew how to make me forget about it for a while. Sometimes when I would tell her that my parents are arguing she would say you want me to spend the night or you want to spend the night at my house. That was nice that she would offer and that is why she was my best friend, but she knew I wasn't about to go anywhere when they are arguing. I also didn't want her to spend the night either I just wanted them to stop before it got out of hand. I knew she wasn't asking so that she could be nosey but so that she could just to be there for me. I had told her that when other people are around my stepfather didn't like to fight, he would never hit or argue with my mother in front of people. After a while even that changed I guess they didn't consider my best friend a stranger anymore. My parents never physically had a fight in front of her but they most certainly argued. My best friend never said anything or told anybody and never stop wanting to come over my house either. She knew it really bothered me so she would try to say something like "girl everybody parents fight".

Now my brother handled it in a different way, he kind of rebelled. He stayed in trouble at school and he began drinking and smoking weed very young. My stepfather pretty much gave him a pass on everything he did and allowed him to freely do it. So in my brothers eyes he couldn't get no better, he thinking pops cool as hell. Reality was my stepfather would eventually use that to his advantage. Now he could go to my brother and get him on his side and hopefully that would stop my mother from leaving or help get her back when she did leave. A few times my brother would say he didn't want to go or he would flat out say he wasn't going. He would say things like it don't' matter we just gone come right back and, he would tell my mother that she just needed to talk to my stepfather. Sometimes my mother would cuss at my brother and tell him that he didn't have a choice, he was going. There were other times when she would seem like she just didn't have no more fight in her and she would just look at him and say ok we not going nowhere.

I would be totally confused because I was always ready to go with my mother even though I felt the same way my brother felt at times. Those times I guess she felt as if she needed to trick my brother so instead of leaving that night we would just leave the next day because she wasn't going to leave him there. She would act like we are going to visit my grandma. I always knew what time it was when she would come in my room and say you should grab a few things in case you want to spend the night with your cousin. When we would get to my grandma house that's when she would say we are staying. My brother would act like it's not a big deal but last night at home he gave her such a problem about leaving. One time my brother didn't want to leave and my mother just took me and we went to my grandmother house. My grandmother was mad that she didn't make my brother come too. My mother said she was tired of arguing with my brother about it and she just wanted to hurry up and get out of there. She told my grandmother she will have one of my uncles go and get him the next day.

Later that night Ron(stepfather) and my brother came over my grandmother house to pick us up, pretty much like they were going to make us go back. My brother was driving and clearly my stepfather had been drinking, who knows maybe my brother was drinking too because he was really being disrespectful to my mother and grandmother. My brother came in my grandmother house telling my mother that they came to get us and that my stepfather said it was time to come home. Before my mother could say anything my grandma began to speak asking my brother just who did he think he was talking to. He told my grandma that he was tired of this and that my stepfather didn't even do anything to my mother. My grandma didn't say another word to my brother she went outside to cuss my stepfather out. She began yelling saying your grown ass sent this boy in here to get her, leave these kids out of it and leave my daughter alone she ain't going nowhere.

Ron is trying to talk to my mother asking her to just get in the car so they can talk. My mother is saying that she doesn't want to talk and to leave her alone. She tells my brother to get out the car and come in the house and he said no. He said he was not going to leave my stepfather like that because he had been drinking and couldn't drive and that my mother just needed to get in the car. My mother and brother go back and fourth for a minute until my grandmother gets fed up and tells my stepfather either you gone leave or I'm going to call Tj and he gone make you leave. Tj is my uncle and he was young and didn't play about his sister neither did my other uncle Dw. My stepfather said well you gone have to do what you got to do because I'm not leaving without my wife. When my grandma asked for somebody to hand her the phone my mother said hold on ma let me just go talk to him for a minute so he will go ahead and leave.

When my mother got in the car they all started yelling for me to come get in the car, saying hurry and get in so we can go. I froze I mean I didn't move at all I just stood there on the porch like what is going on, everyone was yelling. The people in the car yelling for me to get in and the people on the porch yelling for my mother to get out the car. Then Ron started telling my brother to just pull off. My grandma stood in front of the car and said you gone have to run me over then, because you not pulling off with my daughter in this car. My brother is yelling "grandma move I don't want to run you over", when he said that it pissed my uncle Dw off and he began to punch my brother in the face through the window. When my grandmother was trying to stop my uncle, my brother was able to pull off and we went back home.

CHAPTER 5

"It's Not Going To Change"

After that crazy ordeal at my grandmothers house there was a nice time frame that went by where there was no major arguments or physical abuse so that was nice and peaceful. As soon as I got used to the calmness, the darkness would soon show its ugly little head again. I couldn't even tell you what this fight was about, all I know is when the nighttime came, the darkness happened and my mother has a black eye in the morning. I hugged her so tight as tears ran down my face and she said baby I'm ok this will heal. Right after that my uncle Tj moved in with us, I figured it was because of her eye, I was hoping it was because of her eye. When I asked my uncle why did he move in, he told me some crazy story like he couldn't stay with my grandma, I thought it was strange but maybe he didn't know about her eye. I was happy he was there so it didn't matter whatever the reason was. It was cool having him there everything just felt right you know, no fighting and I was sleeping peaceful at night. They had little arguments about petty stuff and about letting my brother and uncle see her car after she had already told them no. Arguments like that are normal, no big deal, those are not going to lead to a fight or anything like that. Don't get me wrong I didn't think every time they argued it would lead to a fight so I wasn't a nervous kid or anything like that. I just was cautious of the fact that it could happen.

After awhile that peace faded because my uncle moved out, he and my mother got into a huge argument about him driving her car. My uncle had an accident in her car after she told him he couldn't use it, so she thought he had just took her keys. She was so mad, once she calmed down, she finally realized what my uncle was trying to tell her. My stepfather told my uncle to take the car after she told him no. At that point it didn't matter anymore because my uncle had already moved his stuff. My grandmother said that was my stepfathers plan the whole time. My stepfather knew if he continued to give my uncle her car after she said no, eventually she would get mad at my uncle and want him to leave. Once you think about it, grandma was on to something, because that's pretty much what happened and now, he has his house all back to himself.

Sure enough the rage is back and he is able to yell like he wants and hit her if wants. I'm up listening waiting for the moment I think I should run in the room. Then it gets quite, my heart is beating fast what should I do, seconds feel like hours then I hear my mothers voice, what a relief I slide down the wall to sit on the floor. When the morning comes I rush to look at my mother and I don't see a black eye or busted lip so that's good maybe I was tripping, but her cheek is a little red. I said ma your face is red what happened, she said nothing and before I knew it I said yea nothing, I heard ya'll last night. She said why wasn't you asleep and I said I don't sleep that much I wake up a lot every time I hear something. Once that happens it is hard for me to go back to sleep. She looked at me and said it's this house it's old and makes all kinds of noises that's probably what you hear. What you think about us moving into a new house my mother asked me. I replied just us, she said what you mean silly I'm talking about all of us, we about to buy a house.

My mother said don't worry everything is going to be ok, things are going to be different I promise, no more noise in the middle of the night. I looked at my mother and said oh that's what it is, the house is making noises. Sometimes it sounds like you and dad are arguing and fighting and that's why I can't sleep. I was so proud of myself I finally said it. Then I thought, oh man I hope I don't get in trouble because she just paused with this look on her face I can say I have never seen before. She took a deep breath and said I know you hear us and I'm sorry for that. I said ma you don't have to be sorry it's not your fault, I don't ever want to make you feel bad. Just like I thought speaking up hurt my mothers feelings and that's the last thing I wanted to do, I felt like such a jerk.

My mother wasn't mad at me but I could tell she didn't want to finish talking about it and she had a sad look on her face. I was ok with that because I didn't want to continue to talk about it either. At that moment I told myself it would be for the best if I just continued to act like I really didn't know what was going on. My mother and I didn't bring the conversation back up again, I guess we both knew it made the other one uncomfortable. The next time they got into a fight my mother packed us up and said we were going to a shelter. I was happy my brother was going to be with me but he said he didn't want to go he was very uncomfortable. My mother changed her mind and said we were just going to go to my grandmothers house until the morning. When we got to my grandmothers house my mother let her know what was going on. My grandmother told her to stay there but my mom said no because she just needed time to think and wanted to be alone. My grandmother wanted her to leave me there too, but I cried to go with my mother, I felt like she didn't need to be alone. We stayed at the shelter for about two nights and then my mother decided we were going to a motel. I guess she just wasn't ready to face it yet and accept that it could happen again.

At the shelter they give you that first night to kind of settle in, they don't ask you to converse with the other ladies or anything if you don't want to. If you want to just stay in your room and get your thoughts together you can. Once you have that moment to yourself the next day they start to encourage you to speak with the other ladies. They start telling you everyone here is going through the same thing and nobody is judging you. Everyone seemed nice but I thought to myself man they all seem battered or torn down in some way. You could see the sadness in their eyes. Some women freely shared their stories and you would be amazed at some of the things these women have went through. They would share with you the reasons why they stayed for so long and the reason they finally had enough. I think some of the stuff was too much for my mother or maybe she wasn't ready to realize that those ladies are her and she is them. The counselor tried to encourage my mom to stay but she said it was for the best, she was going to stay with her sister.

That wasn't true though she rented a room at a motel. I asked why we didn't stay at the shelter she just said well now you can watch what you want on tv and we can go get some food and snacks. She looked at me and said you didn't like it there anyway did you and I said no not really but as long as I'm with you I don't care. After about 3 days she started back talking to my stepfather on the phone and 2 days later we went back. I guess we needed to go back anyway so I could get back to school. This was my last year in middle school and I couldn't miss a lot of days toward the end, at least that's what my mother said. We back now and just like usual everything was cool and back to normal I guess. I'm just waiting to see what gift she is going to get this time. After a couple of weeks go by my parents let me know that we will be moving. They found a house and things will be different. I asked what is going to be different they both gave me a look and said everything, from the look I got from my mother I knew I'd better leave it alone. I seen it in her face she knew I was trying to be a smart ass.

CHAPTER 6

"Domino Affect"

The house they found was nice, it was on a quiet street and it was in the area of the high school that I wanted to attend. Everything was nice and cool for a little while, My parents were even trying to slow up on drinking and they seemed to be doing a good job at it. When they didn't drink a lot they didn't argue as much and when they did argue it didn't go as far as physical violence. Oh, I may have forgotten to mention my parents seemed to have had a drinking problem, when they start, they drink a lot. They met in rehab and somehow they fell in love with each other. Me and my brother knew that and we talked to my mother about it so we didn't mind that and never judged him for it either. I say that just to give you a little insight on how bad the arguments could get and how fast they could happen out of nowhere when they were drinking. At one point they even stopped drinking. That's when you could really see that they were good for each other at least when they weren't drinking, they seemed to bring out the best in one another.

Despite how they met they really and truly loved each

other and did a good job of building each other up. On a different note they feed off each other as well with their addiction to alcohol. When one starts back drinking then eventually the other one starts back. Just like with any addiction it brings ugliness, pain, and chaos. At first, it's fun they start taking a couple of drinks at a time, so you know they still in a happy place, dancing, listening to music and reminiscing on old times. That was ok, I never mind those times in fact some of those times are very beautiful memories for me. It's when a couple of drinks turn into a couple of bottles and that turns into a couple of days at a time, is when stuff starts to get ugly. That's the problem with people that have an alcohol addiction once they really get started or some sort of a crisis happens, really disruption of any kind can get it started, then they no longer have a limit. That's when the petty arguments start to happen, you know what used to be a joke has now became an insult. When the arguments continue into the night the violence always follows.

Domestic Violence affects children in many different ways and affected my brother and I in different ways. By the time we moved in the new house my brother was a teen father, out on his own and abusive to the mother of his child. He also went on to be abusive to many other women he was in relationships with. It's funny how sometimes they would try to tell him that what he did was wrong, but he was only doing what he saw. Let's just be honest that's probably why half of the time they didn't say too much of anything about what he was doing, and when they did it wasn't enough. My mother would tell me that my brother girlfriends were crazy for staying with him and to never let a man put they hands on me. You know what's funny my stepfather even used to tell me that, wow how ironic is that. I would say to my stepfather it's a lot of fighting going on around here. See I could say that to him and not get in trouble because he didn't see that as being disrespectful. He always encouraged me to speak my mind to anyone including him. He would try to act like I was only talking about my brother and his situations. So, I would tell him I am talking about y'all too, then he would immediately apologize saying baby girl I'm sorry we gone do better. I would say ok and walk away feeling a little lied too.

There are many ways that Domestic Violence affects the children. Sometimes they begin to react and look at situations the same way the women or men who are victims in some cases do. They can even take on the trait of the abuser and become very aggressive in their relationships when they don't feel like something is right. I feel as though I took on the trait of the victim far as being accepting to the apology just to make things better even though I thought it would happen again. I feel my brother took on the trait of the abuser because he became abusive to the women he was in relationships with. I really did wish things would get better I loved my stepfather and when they weren't fighting, I loved my mother and my stepfather together. They really did provide a good home for us and that is what's so confusing, because I know your mother being beat up by your father is not providing a good environment for your children.

My brother was back at home for awhile and since he had

already been out on his own before and plus had a child, they helped him get an apartment. I was kind of sad because at least my brother would be there if they were to start fighting. Lately they haven't been fighting so hopefully it stays like this. But I guess that old saying is right " All good things come to an end" because the fighting started back. I wake up one morning getting ready for school and my mother is acting weird, like she not really saying too much, and she had like a mad look on her face. When we get in the car, I keep looking at the side of her face and I finally say why your face look red and puffy. She simply replied leave it alone. I knew what that meant, so I just sat back thinking here we go again. I asked her if she was alright and she said yea its ok its nothing. As we got closer to the school my heart began to feel heavy. I didn't want to go to school anymore I just wanted to be with her. I said Ma are you going to be alright if I go to school, she said yea. I am going to take your Auntie somewhere so I will be gone for a few hours.

When we got to the school, she looked at me and said I Love You I'm ok. I just sat there and she said go ahead and get out the car. I finally said I don't want to go, can I please go with you. She must have seen the hurt in my eyes and without hesitation she said sure baby you can go with me. We pulled off and I sat back in the seat with relief that I was with her. Then she looked at me and said you don't have to worry I'm ok, I looked at her with tears in my eyes and said ok. She grabbed my face and said look we gone have fun today and baby don't say nothing to your Auntie, I said ok. I wasn't going to say anything I just wanted to be with her, I always went into protection mode when they would fight. Even though I couldn't do anything physically I always felt if I was there things would end up ok. I would have terrible thoughts in my mind of things that I wanted to do to protect her and I knew eventually one day I would have to, so I needed to be ready.

When we got home it was a little earlier than the time it would be for me to get out of school, my stepfather said you got out of school early baby girl, I said nope. Before I could say anything else my mother said she got to the school and didn't want to get out. I hear him whisper to my mom did you tell her, and she said no I didn't. He said is everything ok at school that's not like you. I said I seen mama face and I just wanted to be with her. Before he could open his mouth my mother chimed in and said oh girl you should have said something. I would have told you I'm getting an abscess, my tooth on that side has really been bothering me. My stepfather had a surprised and shameful look on his face at the same time. He walked up to my mother and kissed her and said I have to tell you something in the room. When they went in their room I stood at the door and listened. He was apologizing for hitting her and thanking her for not telling me, she was just saying ok ok. I hurried away from the door so they wouldn't catch me listening and they came out acting like nothing never happened.

My mother just looked at me and smiled as she gave me a little hug as she walked passed my chair. We had an understanding that didn't need to be said. I knew why she said all of that about the abscess and me just not wanting to get out the car. Me and her know what really happened at the school. So yea technically I didn't want to get out the car, but she knew the real reason why. She just wanted to keep the peace, so it was no need to bring that back up, and it worked so I was cool with that. Mama started to cook dinner, we laughed and joked and went about the rest of the day like it was a normal day. We did a lot of that type of pretending when things went wrong. I always said to myself once we made it through a storm who wants to go back in if we don't have to. See I always called their fights storms because sometimes they would happened so fast or you could just see it brewing. Just like a storm sometimes they would start out of nowhere and blow over quick. Then sometimes they would last awhile and be very disruptive.

CHAPTER 7

"Mental Roller Coaster"

Now they are back drinking and I am like oh boy here we go, but they promise that they know what they doing. When they would start drinking and I would be looking a certain type of way and in my mind saying why are y'all drinking it's just gone lead to something bad. It's like my mom could hear what I was thinking and she would get frustrated and sometimes mad. She would say stuff like I'm grown and if I want to drink I'm gone drink and I can handle anything that comes with it. I knew she was just lashing out like they say kids do, so I would try to crack a joke or something. I would ask her what's wrong ma why you mad and she would say why you looking at me like you my mama. I would make her laugh by saying I wasn't looking at you like that, I just wanted some, then she would say shut up girl you crazy. I always tried to find a way to lighten the mood. Plus, I'm just a kid what do I know right, maybe it will be different this time. My mother always said sometimes I'm too smart for my own good so hey they adults they should know better.

Then one night the darkness came back. I hear loud voices, loud noises, now it sounds like something breaking, I hear a thump up against the wall I call the police. I run in their room and say I called the police they on they way. My mother said you didn't I said yes, and they said they coming as I began to cry. My stepfather looked at me and said why baby girl, you shouldn't of done that. I am standing there crying and nervous saying I'm sorry, but I was scared, they both looked at me and said scared or what. I didn't know how to answer at that point, so I just said I don't know. My mind is playing tricks on me, it did sound like they were arguing, even the room looks like they were fighting but they are acting like I did something wrong.

When the police came my stepfather said it was all just a misunderstanding and I called by accident. The police looked at my mother who didn't have any marks on her just redness on her face and neck plus she looked disheveled and asked Mrs. Are you ok? She hesitated for a minute and said yea I'm ok, I think we just scared her with all the noise. He shined his flashlight in her face and gave her one more look over and said ok maybe y'all should try and keep it down. The female police office looked at me and said sweetheart are you ok, I didn't say anything as tears began to run down my face. She said its ok you won't get into trouble you can say what happened. The man police officer shined his light in my face and said is it anything you need to tell us before we leave, you just got scared right. I just put my head down and didn't look back up. So, the female officer said ok how about this, Mrs. do you have somewhere to go for the night and my mom said yes. So, she said ok then why don't you just leave for tonight and let things cool off. My stepfather said nothing is wrong, so nobody has to go anywhere, the female officer said I know and I believe you. It would just make me more comfortable if she just left for a minute and y'all give each other some space. When she said that the man officer said in his opinion it was up to my mother, if she didn't want to leave than she didn't have to. My mother said I think I will just leave for a minute she looked at my stepfather and said its ok I will be back.

My mother never yelled at me for calling the police but I felt like a fool and a big jerk. It seemed like I just caused all this mess for nothing and everybody else police included acting like it's not a big deal. We went to a motel that was around the corner from us and stayed there for the rest of the night. I was very quiet because I was trying to figure out if I had done the right thing or not. I thought I did the right thing because he was hurting my mother, but then I thought I didn't because now we are at this room and it didn't seem like my mother wanted to leave. My mother must have noticed I was sad and she said hey you know what this is going to be our girls night. Let's go get some food and we will watch a movie and you can tell me all about the little boy you like, we will go home in the morning ok. I looked at her with tears in my eyes and I said I'm sorry mom, she said for what. I said for calling the police I shouldn't have done that. My mother said I'm not mad at you and he's not mad at you, come on now you know he can't be mad at you. She said don't worry it's gone be ok, lets call and check on him. My mother called him and told him that I was sad and that I thought he was mad at me. They continued to talk for a moment while I just sat there thinking oh no why did she say I thought he was mad at me. I don't know why but I didn't want him to think that, but I still wanted to know if he was mad.

I heard her tell him that we were going to stay until the morning and have a girls night. Then I started to get nervous thinking that he was going to think I did that on purpose. She told me to get the phone he wanted to talk to me, man it was only a couple of steps to get to the phone but it seemed like it took me forever. When I got on the phone, he didn't sound mad at all, in fact he said he wanted me and my mother to have fun. He said tell her I said "to get you anything you want to eat and some snacks", I said ok. Then he said stop sounding sad baby girl I'm not mad at you and I will see you in the morning. Before he hung up, I said dad are you mad at mama, he said no I just want y'all to come home in the morning.

I was really confused then because nobody said I did the right thing, but they didn't say I did the wrong thing either, just that they weren't mad. Which made me come to the conclusion that they thought I was wrong, and they just didn't want to say because I already felt so bad for doing it. The morning came and we went back home and he greeted us with hugs and kisses like nothing ever happened. These are the times that I wanted to talk about things, like tell me what happened but nobody said anything. I'm thinking to myself like I know they have to know I'm confused. I don't really know how to process what happened, but I guess it's better if they don't bring it back up. I went through my childhood kind of putting my feelings on the back burner because I just didn't want to start anything. Which lead me to being kind of an introvert. Throughout the years I called the police a few more times and each time we never did talk about it.

We lived next door to an old couple and sometimes the wife would try to get my mom to open up about what was going on. I thought she was genuinely concerned about my mother. She would see my mother and ask her, are you ok and my mother would always say yea I'm ok there is nothing to worry about over here, how you doing. My mother would come in the house and say she just trying to be nosey because she seen the police over here last night. One day I said to my mom maybe she likes you and she really is concerned. She told me that lady not concerned about me she don't know me, she just want something to talk about. She said people sound like they care then they spread your business all through the neighborhood. She said she got enough of that in the old neighborhood. I was thinking to myself if anyone was talking it must have been my stepfather friends. I never said anything and I know my brother wouldn't have said anything. Our old neighborhood was the neighborhood my stepfather grew up in and he still had a lot of friends there, so maybe they was talking because of stuff he told them. It didn't really matter because at the end of the day it still wouldn't be his fault. It just was one of those things that you wished people wouldn't talk about even if they knew what was going on like Don't Ask Don't Tell type of situation.

Each new year I would wish for a year of them not fighting, until I started to realize that it just wasn't going to happen. Each time I called the police I became a little more discouraged to call them again. It just seemed like she must have to be half dead for them to arrest him. It even started to seem as if they would take their time getting there. Can you believe one time they didn't even come. That time I thought dang somebody could have been getting killed. When I didn't call the police I would call my grandmother and tell her what was going on. She would have me put my mother on the phone and then my mother would end up handing my stepfather the phone. He would start to sound like he was about to cry as he was talking to my grandmother saying he was sorry. If my Uncle Tj would happen to answer the phone he would be yelling and screaming for me to tell him this and that, I would being saying I'm scared. I didn't want to tell him that my Uncle was saying that he was going to fuck him up and kill him. I was thinking what if he got madder who was going to stop him, my Uncle still had to get there. When my Uncle would see me he would say why you didn't tell that muthafucka what I said. He said he wasn't going to do nothing to you because I would have buried his ass for sure. I never was afraid of him doing something to me, I was afraid that one day he would kill my mother and nobody would be there.

CHAPTER 8

"Eyes Open"

I was awaken in the middle of night by the most horrific scream I had ever heard. I immediately sat up in my bed shaken to my core, oh God that's my mama. I ran to my parents room and my stepfather had my mother pent down on the bed and he was squeezing her foot. See my mother had an injury to her foot and she had stitches in her foot like between her toes and he was squeezing that foot. Blood was running down her foot and she was screaming in agony saying please let me go. I yelled out stop dad you hurting her as I pulled on his arm. It was like he was in a daze his eyes looked blank and he wasn't hearing me. My mother is just laying there screaming in pain pleading for him to let her go. I have to do something and I have to do it quick! I run to the kitchen and I get the biggest knife I can find I squeeze the handle tight as I run back in the room. As I approach the room I take a deep breath I run in with the knife in the air screaming let her go. My mother screamed no baby no wait, he looked up and said what are you doing baby girl with a sinister look in his eyes. I am shaking and crying saying let her go I will do it, I will, please don't make me do it.

All of a sudden he let her foot go and said I'm sorry baby girl. I ran over to my mother and hugged her so tight I kept saying why would you do this. My mother needed a towel to stop the bleeding and for the first time ever I was afraid to walk pass him. I was yelling at him get out of here get out, he turned and walked out the room. I ran to get the towel and ran back in the room and closed the door. He finally left out the house, I ran to look out the window to see if he pulled out the driveway. I made sure all the doors were locked and I told my mother that he was gone. I stayed up all that night I could not wait until the daylight came. It was something about the nighttime that made me feel like anything could happen. The demons always come at night along with the darkness. My mothers foot was so swollen and purple she said she needed to go to the hospital to have it checked. I asked her again, why would he do that and she just said I don't know and didn't say anything else. I just left it alone, she was already in pain and someone who said they love her did that. I didn't want to continue to ask her and be another person who causes her pain and heartache.

When my stepfather came home, he came in totally different he was back nice, sounding so apologetic to my mother and even me. He just kept trying to talk to my mother and she told him she didn't want to speak with him right now, she just wanted to go to the hospital. He volunteered to take her and she said no that's alright. He tried to persuade her by saying don't you drive with that foot, I'm sorry let me make it up to you. My mother said that's ok, I'm just going to take baby

girl and I will be alright. My stepfather asked her if she was going to come back, "are you going to leave me" he said and she
said "no, I will be back". I thought maybe she was just saying
that so we could get out of the house without any problems,
but she was serious we were going back. The doctor said that
a few of her stitches had actually come apart. The doctor and
the nurse kept asking her how it happened and she just said
she didn't know, she hit her foot on something and the next
thing she saw was blood everywhere. They looked like they
didn't believe a word she was saying but all they could do was
ask. The doctor said usually bumping your foot against something will not cause this much swelling and your stitches to
come out. The nurse came in and gave my mother a number
to a women's shelter and said this is only if you need it and my
mother said thank you.

When we got back home my stepfather was acting all nice
telling her to put her foot up and don't try to move, he will
get anything she needs. My mother was a little dry with him,
but she was still talking to him. I thought for sure she was going to leave him, but she didn't and this turned into another
one of those situations that we didn't talk about. I thought
because I pulled that knife on him, they were going to say
something, but they didn't. The only thing my stepfather said
about that was "Baby girl don't ever be scared of me I will
never do anything to hurt you." I guess he thought hurting
my mom wasn't hurting me. I began to realize they are missing a big part of the picture, and that is, I am hurt!! I kept
thinking to myself, I need to say something maybe that's why
they don't think it bothers me. Maybe if I mope around and

continue to act sad for along time they will see that it bothers me. I couldn't do that though, because that's just not what
we do. We bounce back we move on and pretend as if nothing happened and then eventually we will forget it happened.
The problem with me was I bounced back I moved on even
pretended as if nothing happened but I could never forget it.

Sometimes I could look at my parents or a certain spot in
the house and I could visualize the fights happening all over
again. My mother would catch me daydreaming as they call
it and would ask me what I was thinking about and I would
say nothing. If I was able to keep seeing those visions why
couldn't they? I started to realize that my feelings or emotions
didn't really mean anything in those circumstances. No matter how hard I cried or how many times I asked them not to
fight they just continue to do so. The fact that I just pulled
a knife on my father and nobody is talking to me about it is
absolutely crazy. I thought am I crazy why isn't this making
sense to me. Everybody tells me how smart I am but doesn't
anyone think I am smart enough to know this isn't right. I
think my mother was so caught up in the pain of it all that
she just honestly didn't see the affect it was having on me. I
think my stepfather was so caught up in the embarrassment of
it all that he didn't want to acknowledge it was affecting me.
Acknowledging it means it's time to take responsibility for
your actions and I think neither one of them were for ready
for that.

My stepfather would have to admit that he was a woman
abuser and what man wants to admit that. My mother would

have to admit that she is an abused woman and she needs to get out of this relationship. I guess I didn't help the situation by acting like it didn't bother me. I wanted everything to be alright so I would hug my mother and tell her that I was ok, as long as she was ok. When she would ask if I was ok, I always said yea even when I was scared. I would even console my step-father when he would be crying and apologizing to her and telling him that everything would be ok. I think my Uncles noticed something was bothering me and when they asked me if I was ok, I knew they were really concerned but I still kept it to myself. They knew I saw a lot more fights or the fights were worse than I said they were but they didn't push it. My Uncle Dw would always say "hey niece you know you can tell me anything and I will make it ok". He was always gentle with the way that he spoke to his nieces, but I knew what that meant, because that's just how my uncles were. My Uncle Tj would just come flat out and say tell me what really happened so I can go fuck him up. You see I didn't want anybody to feel bad and I definitely didn't want anybody to get hurt, so I just kept quiet and acted like everything was always just fine. On the inside I would be screaming say something so they could make my mama leave.

As the years went on, I started to fear that one day he would kill her. I would often think how much more can she take. They started to play all these movies on TV about DOMESTIC VIOLENCE and for some strange reason they became my favorite things to watch. In the movies some of the women stories would have good endings. They would get the strength and power to leave, they would move away and start a whole new life. Although some of the movies didn't end so well. Some of the women were permanently hurt physically for the rest of their lives, some women didn't survive at all and some women ended up killing their abusers. Which all are very horrible outcomes when it seems like something can be done to stop it. Those movies really had my mind going and they kind of made me paranoid too, but I could relate because some were not all that far off from what my mother was dealing with.

CHAPTER 9

"When The Demon Shows Itself"

My Aunt Vi came to live with us for a little while and I thought this is going to be cool. When she lived with us in the past my parents never had physical fights they just argued. Plus, when my mother and aunt are together, they feed off each other strengths and they will always fight for each other. Everything is going good like I thought then my brother moves back in. My brother has become an abuser as well and he has regular fights with his baby mother. We are back to the long nights and the yelling and even the police being called. Even then the police coming meant nothing they never would take anybody sometimes they didn't even make his baby mama go home. That's why eventually it seemed as if they didn't even respond to our address anymore, if they did come it would be like an hour later. I guess they felt they had been out there enough to know that things will probably cool down. My brother battled with a lot of demons of his own from growing up in a home with DOMESTIC VIOLENCE. As you can see, he became an abuser, drug user, and drank alcohol at a very young age. His struggles were a little different from mine because he was a boy. Feeling like he didn't protect his mother affects him way more mentally then it did me.

Boys are raised being told that they are to protect the household, protect your mother and sisters also honor and respect your father. But when it's your father or father figure that is doing the hurting what do they do then. Should that child automatically be expected to know what the right thing to do in that moment is. A child should never be put in the position to make a grown-up decision against a parent figure. As my brother is getting older and coming into his own bits of rage, I don't think my stepfather really wanted him in the house. I could understand why he would feel that way, but in the same instance I thought about what my grandmother always said. She always told my mother "you need to make sure you always got somebody else staying with you because you don't know when he might get mad". After the incident with my mother foot I realized that he could click off or zone out for a minute and that's not good. When I would hear them arguing about my brother moving out, I thought he just was trying to get my mama off to herself, but the only thing with that is Aunt Vi was still there.

There was an altercation that my brother had with one of the neighbors and my stepfather was extremely pissed. Of course, he wanted my brother out the house, but my mom stood her ground and said no, you can leave but he's not. Surprisingly my stepfather didn't go crazy he just asked her a few times to repeat what she said. Then he said "ok, I will leave but you gone regret this". My Aunt Vi and my mother started yelling "what you mean by that", "what you mean by that". I thought to myself this can't be good. This was early in the day when this happened and as the day is going by we haven't heard anything. My mother and aunt were joking like girl he not gone do nothing he probably somewhere getting drunk. I felt like something was strange, no calls or nothing, no constant riding pass the house. Where is he, I thought, either he hurt himself or he will be back. I was hoping he didn't start drinking and get into an accident or something.

That night I asked my mother if I could sleep with her and she said yea. Then she asked why you don't want to sleep in your room, I told her that I thought he was coming back, and he was going to knock on my window. My aunt and mom laughed they said he got keys he will just open the door and besides he somewhere drinking, he not coming back tonight. My mother said "but if you want to, you can sleep with me." I said "ok, but you right I'm going to sleep in my room and if I feel like it I will come in there". We all said good night to each other and went to bed. I laid in my bed and I just kept hearing my stepfather say "you gone regret it". I tossed and turned and every car I heard I looked out the window to see if he was pulling in the driveway. I finally got up and went to lay down with my mother, she teased me as I got in the bed calling me a chicken. I said you not scared, she said no he not gone do nothing and besides your auntie here she will beat him up, we laughed, and I closed my eyes. The comfort of me being next to my mom made me fall into a deep sleep, it was so peaceful and quiet.

I awakened to go and get some water out of the refrigerator, I got my water and I'm about to head down the hallway and I just hear a big boom and crash. I just freeze right there and then I turn to see what it is. It's my stepfather, he jumped through the front window and crashed onto the glass table. He is on the floor trying to shake the glass off and get up. I scream for my mother, her and my aunt are already running out of their rooms because they heard the crash. My brother is running up the basement stairs yelling are y'all ok, my mother yelled go back in the basement, everybody go to the basement. Everything was happening so fast somehow my aunt had gotten a bat and I ran to the room to get the phone to call the police. As I ran back pass to go to the basement, I notice that my stepfather was hurt. He was laying in the glass saying don't call the police. He said please get your mother to help me, he had glass everywhere it was pieces sticking out of his arms. I went to tell my mother what he said, and they thought he was trying to trick me, but I kept telling them no this is serious, he was really not trying to get up.

As they slowly came back up the stairs and took a look they all realized that he did need help. The crazy thing was at that moment it didn't matter anymore how he got hurt, it was just simply he was hurt and everybody started getting towels and trying to see what they could do for him. He didn't want me to call the police but he needed help so I asked if I could just ask for the ambulance. At this point I didn't want to call the police on him, I just wanted him to be ok. Even my aunt was telling him that we not gone let the police take him, but he needs help. He finally agreed to let the ambulance come, he was crying and in a lot of pain. My mother asked him what he was thinking, and he said he knew she wasn't going to open the door and he had left his keys here. He told my mother that he was going to tap on my window, but he didn't want to scare me. Wow I guess jumping through the front window isn't scary at all, I thought to myself.

The ambulance gets there, and they are taking a look at his injuries and taking his vitals. They are asking him questions like what happened and what did he take because his blood pressure and pulse was very high and racing. He denied taking anything and started asking for something for pain. They explained to him that he needed to go to the hospital, and he can get something for pain there. He asked them to remove the glass from his arms there at the house because he didn't want to go to the hospital. The EMT's did not feel comfortable removing some of the glass because they said the pieces could be in a vein or artery and they did not want to risk that because he could bleed out very fast. Plus, they were concerned that his blood pressure was high and his pulse was racing, my mother said she would go with him but he still refused. He told the EMT's that he was ok, and he began to squeeze the bottom of his arm until a piece of the glass popped out and then started pulling other pieces out. The EMT's immediately called the police and said they were going to wait outside in the ambulance until the police arrived.

When the police got there, he had calmed down and removed the glass from his arm and it was wrapped in a towel.

Nobody was acting scared or nervous and my mother was not saying she wanted him to leave so, they didn't have a reason to arrest him. The police also said they could not make him go to the hospital, so they left along with the ambulance. I helped my mother bandage him up and stayed up the rest of the night in disbelief that he did that. My aunt was out done, and she said he did that on purpose because he knew my mother would not make him leave if he hurt his self. I didn't think he tried to hurt his self on purpose. It was the rage that made him jump through the window. I saw the look in his eyes when he was trying to stand up and it was nobody home in those eyes, he had blanked out. My stepfather was a big guy and he had height with it, so it would have been straight survival mode in order to stop him. I was thankful that he hurt his self because it was no telling what he would have done. Somehow the pain from the glass must have snapped him back to reality.

In the morning everybody was slow motion and my stepfather was quiet as a church mouse. When he finally came out of his room, we all asked if he was ok and was telling him that he probably still needed to go to the doctor, but he said no. He apologized to everybody for waking them up last night and that was it. Later they began to even joke about how he crashed through the window. I never thought it was funny at first because I knew the truth, he was going to hurt my mom that night. I'm thinking wow everybody is missing the fact, why did he jump through that window. What was he going to do if he hadn't hurt himself? If you are mad enough to jump through a thick glass window, then you are not just trying to talk. The sad thing is as time went on, I did begin to laugh at some of the jokes, I guess if you can't beat them you join them.

After that incident happened I began to have bad dreams and I would grit my teeth in my sleep. I even started back sleep walking. My mother said she would catch me just walking around the house checking the rooms or standing in their bedroom. I never told my mother about the bad dreams because I didn't want anyone to think I was weird. My dreams would be about me finding her hurt and bloody. I started sleeping at night for only a couple of hours because I didn't want to stay sleep long enough to have the dreams. I didn't really want to go anywhere unless I was with my mother. I just felt like I needed to stay close especially if it was tension between them. When I would spend the night out my nerves would be so bad thinking about what if something happens and I'm not there. I would make sure I call her at night before I went to sleep and the first thing in the morning when I wake up. I remember my mother used to say you just like an old lady you need to have fun. I did have fun sometimes, but it seemed like every time I started to feel like things were normal that's when something would happen. I would just tell my mom that fun to me is hanging out with her and writing.

CHAPTER 10

"When The Demon Returns For Victory"

Writing and reading the newspaper seemed to help the tension go away in my mind. Reading the newspaper helped to clear my mind because then I'm thinking about other peoples issues and problems. At the time, I didn't know why but writing my thoughts down was the best, it helped me feel better, so I kept a journal. My mother thought it was cute that I had a "diary" and she would always buy me those cute little dainty books that said diary on them, and I would just want a spiral notebook. The stuff I was writing down wasn't cute, so why put it in a cute book, so I liked to call them journals instead. My stepfather had given me some books that his mother had that were really cool and looked more like journals. Anything I liked to do or showed interest in he always backed me or supported me on it. He thought it was so intelligent of me to like to write, he would say "she gone be our teacher or lawyer".

One day my mother read some of my journal and they didn't think it was so cute anymore. I would write about the fighting and when we would leave and come back, when my brother would jump on his girlfriends or have one of his flip out episodes, and also about my feelings. My mother asked me "why are you writing that stuff" I told her it was because it made me feel better. Then she asked me "why do you keep it then" I said because sometimes I go back and read it. She told me that I can't hold on to the past and that I have to let it go and move on. She told me that I should throw my journals away, because keeping them and reading them sometimes is just holding on to the past. She said oh that's why you always walking around here acting funny because you keep reminding yourself of peoples mistakes. Then she said, we don't need you judging us around here because everybody not perfect miss lady. I asked her what was I supposed to do then, it's not like I'm telling somebody. I just write it down and read it to myself. She said you better not be telling nobody what goes on in this household, I said I know that.

My mother tells me look, if you have to write it down then write it down but throw it away after, so nobody can find it and you won't make people feel bad. I told her that I understood, and I would throw it away from now on. I also told her that I was sorry if I made them feel bad because I wasn't judging them, I just liked to write. The crazy thing was I didn't understand how that could make them feel bad, but I just rolled with it. The joke around the house became not to do anything around me because I was going to write it down. I didn't know then but now I realize that was my way of letting it go and moving on. When I would go back and read the things that I wrote I wasn't trying to judge them or hold it against them. It was just my way of never forgetting would could happen.

Things did change for a while and I thought wow maybe that was the stopping point. My stepfather finally realized that his anger can get out of control. I had really started to believe that the storm had passed. When they would joke about the window incident, he would say he didn't know what he was thinking he guess, it's just the things you do when you mad. My mother would laugh and say yea next time you jump through a window you gone jump back. They still had arguments like every married couple would, but nothing got serious. Things were going really well with the exception of my brother episodes. I was still having the bad dreams though and I didn't understand why. I wanted to tell my mother about them, but I didn't want her to think that I was trying to start something when everything was going so good. If I had a bad dream more than two times in a week, I would tell her that I had a bad dream, but I would change some of the details. I would never say it was her in the dreams and she would say maybe it was something you watched on television. I would soon find out why the bad dreams didn't stop it was because the storm was not over yet.

One night I'm awaken by my mother yelling what's wrong, what's wrong, what are you talking about. I hear my stepfather say just come on it got to be done. I'm at my room door listening and my mother begins to cry and say please don't do this. When I open my room door, they are beginning to walk down the hallway, my stepfather is behind her and she is crying saying please just talk to me. I said what's wrong, what's going on and I heard my mother say go back in your room and call the police now. My heart started racing she had never told me to call the police before. Before I could move my stepfather said don't call the police baby girl go back in your room it will be ok soon. I grabbed the phone and called 911 please I need the police now. The operator asked what was wrong I told her my mom is crying and told me to call the police my dad is walking her into the kitchen. I was talking so fast the operator said slow down tell me what is going on I said I don't know, she asked, is he hurting her I said I don't know. I picked up my nephew that was sleeping in the bed with me and began to walk toward the kitchen.

My mother is screaming please don't do this, the operator asked is that your mom I hear I said yes, she said don't do what, tell me what's going on. As I got closer, I started to cry and yell on no, please dad don't, don't do it please. I hear the operator say I need you to calm down and tell me what's going on. I said please tell them to hurry he has a gun to my mama head. She said give me the address and stay on the phone. It seemed like it was so many noises I couldn't think straight, me and my mother was yelling, my nephew started crying, and the operator was in my ear saying what's happening, the police will be there soon. My stepfather looked up when my nephew started to cry and said baby girl why you crying. I said I'm scared please don't do this dad put the gun down. He replied "it's gone be ok baby girl you don't have to be scared". He said get up from there, why you right there. We had a sectional couch and I was bent down behind the arm of the couch that

was by the wall, so I had me, and my nephew positioned between the wall and the arm of the couch. I was thinking that
if he was going to shoot me at least I could cover my nephew
and maybe he wouldn't get shot.

When he noticed I had the phone in my hand he said
baby girl who you talking to, don't call the police. My mother
started struggling saying leave her alone she didn't call the police. He pressed the gun up against her head some more and
I yelled "I didn't call the police it was grandma". I hung the
phone up and continued to try and talk to him asking him
what's wrong please dad just tell me what's wrong. I was di-
aling my grandmothers number praying that she would answer the phone and figure out what was going on. He said
baby girl put the phone down don't call nobody. I put the
phone down, but I placed it upwards so if somebody picked
up, they could hear. I kept talking to him very loud and clear
so that my grandmother could understand. I told my mother
that I loved her and don't worry you not gone die today. I
said dad please take the gun from mama's head don't shoot
her in front of me please. I heard my grandmother scream my
name through the phone then she said oh Lord Jesus help me.
My mother was steady begging him to put the gun down. My
stepfather said baby girl I told you don't call nobody hang up,
I hung the phone up. He told my mother that he loved her
and looked at me and said I love you baby girl and pulled the
TRIGGER!! I closed my eyes and slid down the wall with my
nephew in my arms, at that moment I couldn't breathe, then
all of a sudden, I heard my mother yell my name. I opened my

eyes and she was grabbing me, and my stepfather was sitting in the chair at the table crying.

Before my mother could get me up off the floor the police was at the door, she opens the door and let them in and turns to hug me. She yells my brother name and starts toward the basement door, the police officer is saying wait a minute Mrs., she said my son is down there. As the other police officer grabs the gun that's sitting on the table and puts my stepfather in hand cuffs. My mother said please let me go check on my son and the officer told her to stay where she was, and he would go down there and see. He asked what his name was and went downstairs, calling his name and checked his room. He came back and told my mother that nobody was down there. My stepfather looked at my mother and said I'm sorry. They are asking my mother all these questions and shinning their flash-lights around. I couldn't talk it was like I was blank I felt like I couldn't even hear for a minute. The officer was asking if I was the one who called the police, I finally shook my head and said yes it was me and put my head down. The officer looked at me and said good job as one of the other officers was taking my stepfather out.

The police officer told my mother that my stepfather was most definitely going to jail. He also said he didn't know how long they will hold him before he gets bail because he didn't shoot her. My mother said oh, but he pulled the trigger and the officer said excuse me. She said right before ya'll came to the door he had just pulled the trigger and when it didn't shoot, he let me go. The officer said Mrs. you need to come to the station first thing in the morning and press charges. As the officer was about to walk toward the door, I thought to myself, this is the time to speak up and I said WAIT it's more guns I will show you. The officer said you know where more guns are, I said yes, he looked at my mother and said is this true, she replied yes. The officer went to the door and told one of the other officer to come back in, and told them what I said. I took them to my parents room and showed them where the other two guns were at. When they left, I started to cry harder and my mother gave me a hug and said it's gone be ok, it's over now. For some reason I didn't feel like that was the end of it. Plus, I'm still thinking where was my brother?

While the police were there the phone kept ringing, but we didn't answer it, because my mother was talking to the police. The phone rang again as she was talking to me and she answered, I heard my grandmother scream through the phone Thank you God what in the world is going on over there. My mother took a deep breath and said he flipped out again. My mother asked her if my brother was over there and my grandmother said he on his way back to your house. My grandmother must have been fussing at my mother because she kept saying I know ma, I know ma. As my brother was coming through the door my mother told my grandmother she would call her back so that she could talk to him. My mother asked my brother if he was alright and how did he get to my grandmother house. He said he ran half the way and then he saw someone he knew that took him the rest of the way. My brother asked where my stepfather was at and my mother told him in jail, he said good. My brother said man that nigga crazy

I didn't even do nothing to him. My mother said what are you talking about, what happened.

My brother began to tell us that my stepfather woke him up with a gun pointed in his face and told him to get up. He said he sat up quickly and asked, what you doing, and what's going on. My stepfather just kept telling him to get up and go upstairs. My brother said he froze for a minute then he slowly got out of the bed and started walking towards the door. He said his heart was beating so fast and he didn't know what to do. My stepfather was just standing there by the head of his bed as he walked towards the door, he looked back, and my stepfather still had not moved. Once my brother got to the door, he said he just took off and ran out the side door. My mother started to cry and was hugging him saying how sorry she was that he did that to him. My brother asked my mother, why did he do that, and she said "I don't know baby". I chimed in saying he went crazy, he just tried to kill mama in the kitchen, my brother said WHAT in disbelief. So, I began to tell him how I was woken up and the ordeal that happened while he was trying to get to grandma house. My brother thought my stepfather was only trying to hurt him and that's why he ran without even thinking about we were still in the house. I told my brother it was a good thing that he ran because if he would have killed us at least someone was left to say it was him. My mother looked at me and said he wasn't going to kill you, I said we don't know that.

CHAPTER 11

"Denial Causes The Most Pain"

The next day my mother had to go to the police station and press charges which she did. But she said they told her he would not be charged with trying to kill her because the gun was not in his hand when they got there. It also appears that the gun was not working, the firing pin or something like that was broke. Also, the story my stepfather told them was he was showing her the gun didn't work and they needed to get rid of it. He said what I saw was him simply showing her that the gun didn't work, and I must have gotten scared and called the police. My mother also said that they told her that the only way he would probably even be charged with attempt to murder is if I testified in court. When she said that my heart dropped but I said, "mama I will do it". She said, "no I'm not going to put you through that, you shouldn't have to do that". I asked her if they said my brother had to testify, she said no because he was not there when it happened. Testifying was not something that I wanted to do but I knew it was something that I had to do. I told my mother not to worry about

71

me I wasn't scared to say what happened. The only thing that my brother would be able to testify to is when he put the gun in his face. My mother said that they told her even with that he wouldn't be charged with attempt murder, assault maybe.

My mother decided to drop the charges, also to forgive him and stay together. I will never understand why my mother decided to drop the charges and forgive him, only she understands that. Women involved in domestic abuse are often judged for the decisions they make. We are often quick to judge them when they decide to stay, but unless you are in that situation we will never understand. Even I, being raised in that environment still had love for my stepfather after every incident even the one with the gun. I never tried to judge my mother for staying after that, but I did look at my stepfather in a very different way. I still loved him for all the good things he had done and for being a father to me when my biological father wasn't there, but I no longer felt safe with him. I actually had thoughts and dreams about having to kill him. After that incident I never had a restful night of sleep, visions in my head and sounds in the night kept me awake. I was always waiting for the next time when the gun would work.

I started to sneak and smoke black & mild cigars as a way to help me relax. I became even more secluded staying in my room as a way to avoid everyone. No matter what my mother was dealing with she was still big on us being respectful and I just didn't care anymore. My mother always said she could tell what I was thinking by the look on my face, so if that was true, I thought it be best that I stay out the way. I no longer wanted to talk to my stepfather or to pretend like everything was ok. I used to always want to hear my stepfather's side of the story, so that I could try to understand why he would hit my mother. This time I didn't care, it didn't matter to me what he had to say. All that matter now was the visions I kept seeing in my head and every time that I would relive that night in my head. I realized that my feelings didn't matter, and tears certainly meant nothing. I decided that I wouldn't let anyone see me cry again because it means nothing. I had got tuff it's time to grow up, I just might have to break free. I went from being very talkative around the house to just being quiet. My stepfather would ask if everything was ok because it seemed like I had something on my mind. He was right I had disconnected, I had destruction on my mind. I simply answered I'm good and nothing else. I even started to have a disconnect with my brother. The more I struggled with the thoughts in my head I began to look at them all different. How can they act like nothing happened, that night changed me and it should have changed them also.

I began to feel frustrated and uneasy on the inside all the time. I was frustrated because I wanted somebody to notice that my personality had changed. I wanted them to say that he tried to KILL them, and he is back here living with us like it was a water gun. I wanted my stepfather to say that he was going to KILL them that night and acknowledge the TERROR he put in me that night. But they didn't they just did what made them feel better and that was to act like nothing happened. Nobody even thought enough or cared enough to ask how I was dealing with it. My stepfather had to go to a couple of DOMESTIC VIOLENCE classes, but I don't think he took it serious. He would talk about how the classes were stupid and the men in there was fucked up but never that he got something good out of it. He didn't even feel like he should have to go to those classes.

Now I am starting to press the limits, I am smoking cigars more and even drinking. I am getting so bold with it that I am smoking black & mild's in my room with my face out the window. I guess I wasn't that bold with it because I didn't want to get caught, but I didn't care if I got caught either. I was even going in the basement smoking down there and asking my brother for some of his liquor. Eventually I got caught smoking in my room and they said we needed to have a talk to find out why I was doing that. I thought oh so they do care, I didn't worry about getting in trouble I was just happy they noticed. Finally, they will see I am having trouble coping with this. My parents sit me down and say you know you too young to be smoking why are you doing that. They said you better than that baby girl this ain't you what's going on? I began to tell them that the cigars help me relax when I feel tight and frustrated. My mother asked me if I was stressed about school, I laughed. I never had a problem with my grades even with me missing a lot of days. I said, "no I'm stressed about ya'll". This pretending we do is frustrating we just always act like nothing happens and it's bothering me. They had the nerve to say, "what are you talking about". In that moment I thought to myself here is your chance, no more pretending just say it, if they won't. So, I told them how since he tried to KILL them, I have had trouble sleeping. My stepfather said I was not going to KILL them, and I wasn't going to hurt you either, my mother chimed in and said I told her that. Wow I thought to myself are they crazy, his actions proved what he was trying to do. I told them that when I drink that's the only time I feel comfortable around them. My mother told me that I was taking it too far and trying to use that for as an excuse to do what I wanted to do, it ain't like he pulled the gun on me.

They really think it had no affect on me at all or they too caught up in denial to accept that it happened and it's not right. As I began to get frustrated and felt like I wanted to scream I looked at my stepfather and asked him if I could smoke right now, he said yes. Of course, he would say yes, he doesn't want to go any further with this conversation. My mother said you can smoke your little cigars, but you are not going to be drinking. Believe it or not I didn't want them to agree with that I wanted them to acknowledge this is a problem due to the violence that's going on in here. I didn't have to be hit to experience the pain of it, I didn't have to have the gun pointed at me to feel like I was going to die. Say that gun would have worked and he succeeded in what he was going to do but never pulled the gun on me, maybe he would have even killed himself also that night who knows but all I know is I still would have died that night as well. Mentally and emotionally I would have been dead.

How would anyone be able to go on living life normal after that. They are acting like I'm supposed to feel like he was doing me some big favor by not pointing the gun at me. I wish I could forget it. I wish it never happened, but it did.

My mother was right I was using it as an excuse. At least when I had something to drink, I could sleep and not have any dreams. The thing that is confusing to me is, that is my reality everyday and night since that happened so is it an excuse or is it the truth. My mother told me that she was disappointed and that I was better than that. She told me that I have a strong mind and I'm smart and that I don't have to turn to drinking to get through anything. She said that's why she doesn't worry about me because she knows I will be ok. The crazy thing is I wanted her to worry I needed her to worry because I wasn't dealing with it well. I just wanted to break down and scream I'm scared, and I don't know what to do, but I didn't. I felt like what difference did it make I have already said enough and they still not realizing it. It's not like I said I'm doing this to have friends or to be cool. I'm doing these things so that I can feel shut off around them. I guess I still didn't want to hurt my mother feelings so I said she was right and I would not drink anymore. I know I was lying and after that I didn't speak of that night again.

I continued to smoke cigars of course and I was drinking any chance I could get. The longer I continued to drink, it no longer had the same affect on me. Drinking used to make me numb to my feelings, I was able to shut them off and just be there. Now when I have a drink, I can still see the visions and it's making me angry. So, when they are getting along laughing and joking with each other I am thinking negative thoughts in my head. I am no longer happy when my family is getting along. I just look at them and think they are being fake and probably just waiting for the next time something should happen, I am too. I am just waiting thinking of what I will do, and what I could grab. I started to speak my mind more about DOMESTIC VIOLENCE, always having an opinion on how it disgusted and angered me. During that time, it was a lot of situations happening that were recognized on the news regarding DOMESTIC VIOLENCE or women being shot by men they are in relationships with. I began to watch a lot of movies about DOMESTIC VIOLENCE some based on real life events, and it just made me so angry and scared. Women were losing their lives due to DOMESTIC VIOLENCE and I spared no expense voicing my opinion around the house. My family seemed to think those movies were to raw for me and maybe I shouldn't watch them. Those movies were my reality in a sense and it allowed me to see that a lot of women go through this and it has to stop, they have to get out.

There was another episode of VIOLENCE that happened which I knew it would be, but what I didn't know, was that it would be the last. I did not hesitate to call the police and they took him to jail along with the weapon he chose. This time as usual the demon appears in the night and I jump up to my mother crying. I entered the room and my stepfather was hitting my mother in the head with a wave brush as she was fighting to block his blows. This is not just any brush, it is a big wooden brush that is very solid. Her head was bleeding and I saw that rage in his eyes. I yelled out stop, I called the police and they are on the way. My stepfather stopped swinging the brush and said baby girl we just talking. My mother moved away from him and said they gone take you to jail this time as she was crying. My stepfather looked at me and said I didn't do nothing tell them I didn't do nothing. He always tried to plead his case to me and say he was sorry, or he didn't do nothing. Not this time I have had enough, if this does not stop, he will KILL my mother. I stood their holding a knife as I looked him in his eyes and said I will KILL you, if you hit my mother again, I am tired. I finally broke, I told him that I promise I will KILL you, I can't take anymore. My mother was saying no baby don't say that, put the knife down. She finally decided that was enough and she filed for a divorce. I thought to myself this is the end and she made it out alive. Physically yes, but emotionally and mentally no, Domestic Violence had a long term effect on her as well.

CHAPTER 12

"The Aftermath, Beginning Of A New Journey"

The divorce is just the end of the relationship but not the end of the journey for the women. My mother was scarred physically, emotionally and mentally after that and it showed to be true through her actions and decisions she made moving forward. Never will those who have not went through something like that understand what a victim who becomes a survivor deals with. The aftermath is very real and they have to readapt to a lot of things. Some have to deal with financial and social readjustments that often make them feel as if they have made the wrong decision to leave. I perceive it to be like an addiction. You know it's wrong and harmful to you but the parts of it that make you feel good is what keeps a hold on you. Some are able to overcome that, and some are not which leads them to continue to be in relationships like that or leads them to other forms of abuse. It also can have that same kind of effect on children raised in domestic violent homes. Some become victims or even the abuser in their own relationships. Some can even become shut off or fearful in realizing that not all relationships will have that issue.

Domestic Violence affects children very deeply and emotionally. It is a very scary situation for a child to be in. Even the child you think is the smartest, bravest, and has the strongest mind is scared in that situation. It is very hard for women to see what is right in front of them when they are involved in domestic violence. Because they are in a state of confusion and fear themselves, they just don't realize how the child or children is affected. A lot of people feel if the child is not being hit or verbally abused then it does not have a lasting effect on them. Just like with anything else domestic violence affects different children in different ways, but it does affect them.

My reality is fear that I could be involved in a relationship like that. I would never want to expose my child to that. I would never want to fear the man that says he loves me. My constant fear is that I could be one of the ones that don't make it out alive. I could be one of the ones that spend the rest of my life in prison for defending myself. Those fears overshadow any fear of missing out on love. The aftermath of domestic violence had a negative effect on me and my mother relationship with each other as well. I never judged my mother for staying with my stepfather during those times, but I found myself judging her for the decisions she made once she was out of that relationship. At first, I did not understand that domestic violence was like and addiction and what powerful hold and affect it could have on a person who survived that.

I wanted my mother to blossom and be this big advocate against domestic violence. I wanted her to become an example of how you can be stronger and more stable alone than you ever were in that situation. I wanted her to transform into this person straight out the gate after she got out of that relationship. When she didn't, I was angry that she allowed someone to break her strong spirit like that. She always appeared to be strong when she was with him so now that she is making decisions that I thought a weak mind person would make I would let her know that's how I felt. Because I didn't fully understand at the time that she was still dealing with the emotional and mental affects from domestic violence, I may have lashed out to harshly or spoke too soon or even not spoke soon enough in some situations and that damaged our relationship.

I feel that in order for someone to truly heal from domestic violence they need to go through a recovery phase. I am not a doctor or therapist, but I am someone that witness the effects of it first hand. With any dramatic incident or accident or even illness you go through a recovery phase. In that recovery phase you have to learn how to take care of yourself, build your strength and your health back up. That rehabilitation or recovery time is all dependent on your dedication with some support from others. Everyone is cheering you on, doing what they can to help you get better and having sympathy for you when you don't bounce back as fast. So, I feel the same needs to apply to surviving domestic violence. So, even with that be-

ing said that person still has to have the will power to overcome it.

The recovery phase to me is just simply taking the time to
love yourself and your children if you have them. Not only
does the victim need to start to feel safe again but the children
must learn that as well. A child should always feel peace, hap-
piness, and a sense of restfulness in their home. As a parent
your worse fear is for something to happen to your child and
as a child your worse fear is for something to happen to your
parent. So, a child will always remember seeing their mother
battered and bruised and they will never look at the abuser
the same. A child will begin to battle with thoughts in their
head that they should protect their mother and, also thoughts
of guilt for being afraid to. Those thoughts can break a child
or bring an evil out of them they don't know how to stop.
It could take away the mere innocence of a child and harden
their spirit.

I remember thinking about situations when I did nothing
saying to myself, I should have killed him or at least tried
to do something. Having thoughts of guilt thinking that she
wanted me to help her and I didn't. At times I was mad at
my Grandmother and Uncles because I felt they should not
have listen to my mother and just made him come up missing.
Then I felt guilty and bad that I would even want something
like that to happen to anyone. I became cut off and sheltered
in a sense, I just liked to be in my own thoughts by myself.
Game planning in a way so that the next time I have the opportunity to protect her I will be ready. So that recovery phase

is so very important so that children can start to feel safe and at peace again. You know that saying "they don't have a care in the world" that's how a child's life should be. They should be able to see you smiling and happy not battered and bruised. You have to keep in mind that our children are a part of us so if we are not whole how can our children be.

Even as an adult I have dreams of those acts of violence against my mother. I still to this day have moments of anger thinking about it. My personal experience with growing up with domestic violence has had a lasting effect on me. I am still a very sheltered person, suspicious of anyone who proclaims to love me. Only because I know first hand someone can profess to love you and punch you in the face the next day. I know the affects it can have on a child and I would never want my child to experience that. The dreams still happen from time to time and the visions too. I still have deep feelings of guilt that I felt the way I did and regret that I never took the opportunity to tell them how it really affected me. I hope Domestic Violence does not affect every child that experiences it in the way it affected me but the sad reality is that it can affect a child in an even deeper or worse way then it affected me.

CPSIA information can be obtained
at www.ICGtesting.com
Printed in the USA
LVHW051511090623
749357LV00023B/126